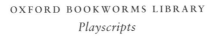

OXFORD BOOKWORMS LIBRARY
Playscripts

Much Ado About Nothing

Stage 2 (700 headwords)

D1447608

Playscripts Series Editor: Clare West

WILLIAM SHAKESPEARE

Much Ado About Nothing

Retold by
Alistair McCallum

Illustrated by
John Dillow

OXFORD UNIVERSITY PRESS

OXFORD

UNIVERSITY PRESS

Great Clarendon Street, Oxford, OX2 6DP, United Kingdom

Oxford University Press is a department of the University of Oxford.
It furthers the University's objective of excellence in research, scholarship,
and education by publishing worldwide. Oxford is a registered trade
mark of Oxford University Press in the UK and in certain other countries

This simplified edition © Oxford University Press 2016

The moral rights of the author have been asserted

First published in Oxford Bookworms 2004

10 9 8 7 6 5 4 3

ISBN: 978 0 19 420954 0   Book
ISBN: 978 0 19 462088 8   Book and audio pack

Printed in China

Word count (main text): 5,793 words

For more information on the Oxford Bookworms Library,
visit www.oup.com/elt/gradedreaders

ACKNOWLEDGEMENTS
Illustrations by: John Dillow/Beehive Illustration

CONTENTS

INTRODUCTION

Much Ado About Nothing is set in Messina, a town on the Mediterranean island of Sicily, about four hundred years ago. Sicily is Italian now, but in Shakespeare's time it had Spanish rulers. When the play begins, the Spanish prince, Don Pedro, and his Italian gentlemen are coming to Messina after fighting in a war. They are going to stay for some time at the house of Leonato, Lord of Messina.

PERFORMANCE NOTES

Act 1 Scene 1: Leonato's garden, outside his house
       Scene 2: A room in Leonato's house
Act 2 Scene 1: A large room in Leonato's house
       Scene 2: A smaller room in Leonato's house
       Scene 3: Leonato's garden
Act 3 Scene 1: Leonato's garden
       Scene 2: A room in Leonato's house
       Scene 3: A street in Messina, with a low wall
Act 4 Scene 1: Outside a church
       Scene 2: In the Messina prison
Act 5 Scene 1: A street in Messina
       Scene 2: Leonato's garden
       Scene 3: A room in Leonato's house

You will need a rolled-up letter, tables and chairs, glasses and bottles, some paper for Verges to write on, masks, and musical instruments. In Leonato's garden there must be a tree to hide behind.

CHARACTERS IN THE PLAY

Leonato, Lord of Messina

Hero, Leonato's daughter

Beatrice, Hero's cousin

Margaret and **Ursula,** Hero's servants

Don Pedro, Prince of Aragon

Benedick, a young gentleman, and friend of Don Pedro's

Claudio, a young gentleman, and friend of Don Pedro's

Don John, Don Pedro's brother

Borachio and **Conrade,** Don John's servants

Father Francis, a priest

Dogberry, the head of the police

Verges, a policeman

Three other policemen

Musicians

Two messengers

'The soldiers are coming back to Messina today.'

MUCH ADO ABOUT NOTHING

This much loved comedy of William Shakespeare's first appeared in print in 1600. It is about two very different love stories. When the handsome Claudio returns from war, he immediately falls in love with the beautiful Hero, and everybody is happy when they decide to marry. Everybody, that is, except one man, who does his best to break the young couple's hearts.

Love, like war, is not easy. It can be very sad, when things go wrong. But it can also be very funny, for family and friends who enjoy watching the young lovers. Benedick and Beatrice are not a sweet, loving couple like Claudio and Hero. They both hate the idea of marriage. 'I shall never be a husband,' says Benedick. And if Beatrice is asked when she will marry, she answers, 'Never, I hope.' But their friends have a secret plan...

ACT 1 SCENE 1

The soldiers come back from the war

Outside Leonato's house, in Messina. Leonato is talking to Hero and Beatrice. A messenger arrives with a letter.

MESSENGER My lord Leonato, this letter is for you.

LEONATO Thank you. (*He reads the letter.*)

HERO What does it say, father? Is it about the war?

LEONATO Yes, my dear. It's from my friend Don Pedro. It says that the war has finished.

HERO That's wonderful news!

LEONATO It says that the soldiers are coming back to Messina today. Don Pedro is coming to see us.

HERO Are many of the soldiers hurt?

MESSENGER No, my lady, only a few.

LEONATO This letter says that Claudio, a young gentleman from Florence, was very brave.

BEATRICE What about the Lion of Messina, the bravest man in the world? (*She laughs.*)

LEONATO I don't understand. Who are you talking about, Beatrice?

HERO She means Benedick, father, a friend of Don Pedro's.

BEATRICE That's right. He thinks that he's the bravest man in the world, but he isn't. He doesn't like fighting. He prefers watching other people fight.

MESSENGER That's not true! Benedick is a good soldier.

HERO   Don't be angry. My cousin Beatrice likes
       Benedick, but she laughs at him all the time.

LEONATO   Here they come! (*Don Pedro, Don John,
          Claudio, and Benedick enter.*) Don Pedro!
          Welcome to Messina!

DON PEDRO   Leonato! It's good to see you again. You
            already know my friend Benedick, don't you?

BEATRICE   Of course he does. Benedick is the most
           famous man in the world. Everyone knows him.

DON PEDRO   And this is Claudio.

LEONATO   Welcome, gentlemen. This is my daughter,
          Hero, and her cousin, Beatrice.

BENEDICK   Ah, Beatrice – we've already met, haven't we?

BEATRICE   Have we? I can't remember. (*All laugh.*)

BENEDICK   You never remember anything, Beatrice –
           you're always too busy talking.

BEATRICE   Perhaps my words are more interesting than
           yours, Benedick. (*She turns away from him.*)

DON PEDRO   Leonato, this is my brother, Don John. He
            was my enemy for many years, but now we are
            friends again.

LEONATO   That's good. Don Pedro, I hope with all my
          heart that you, your brother, and your friends
          will stay here at my house for some time. Would
          you like to come inside?

          Everyone leaves except Claudio and Benedick.

CLAUDIO   Benedick, did you see Leonato's daughter?

BENEDICK Yes, of course I did. Why? Do you like her?

CLAUDIO Like her? I love her!

BENEDICK What? You've only met her once! She's very
    sweet, but…

CLAUDIO Sweet? She's the most beautiful girl I've ever
    seen! Benedick, I'm going to marry her if I can!

DON PEDRO (*Entering*) Come on, you two! Come inside!

BENEDICK Claudio has some interesting news, Don Pedro.
    He's in love.

DON PEDRO Really?

CLAUDIO I love Hero. I want to marry her.

DON PEDRO That's wonderful! I think the two of you will
    be very happy if you marry.

'*I love Hero. I want to marry her.*'

BENEDICK Ha! It's impossible for anyone to be married and to be happy. I tell you, *I* shall never be a husband!

DON PEDRO Oh yes, you will! One day soon, Claudio and I will call you 'Benedick, the married man'. Now, go into the house and tell Leonato that we'll be with him soon.

Benedick leaves. Borachio enters. He hides, and the others don't see him. He listens carefully.

CLAUDIO Don Pedro, you must help me. I love Hero, but I don't know if she loves me. I want to marry her, but perhaps her father won't agree. What can I do?

DON PEDRO Don't worry. Leonato is an old friend of mine. I'll talk to him.

CLAUDIO But what about Hero? I don't know what to say to her. She's so beautiful!

DON PEDRO Listen, there'll be a party here tonight. I'll tell Hero that you love her. I'll ask her if she wants to marry you. She'll say yes, I'm sure.

CLAUDIO Oh, I hope so! Thank you, my lord.

Claudio and Don Pedro leave.

BORACHIO So Claudio wants to marry Leonato's daughter. My master, Don John, will find that very interesting!

ACT 1 SCENE 2

Don John hears a secret

A room in Leonato's house. Don John and his servant Conrade are talking.

CONRADE   What's the matter, my lord? You look unhappy.

DON JOHN   I look unhappy because I *am* unhappy.

CONRADE   But why, Don John? You and your brother Don
          Pedro are friends now.

DON JOHN   Don't talk to me about my brother! I hate him.
          He thinks that we are friends, but I'm still angry
          with him. I'm angry with all of them – Leonato,
          Claudio…

CONRADE   But why?

DON JOHN   Stop asking so many questions, Conrade! My
          brother is my enemy, and so are all his friends.
          Do you understand?

CONRADE   Yes, my lord. But you must try to *look* happy
          if you want your brother to think that you don't
          hate him any more.

DON JOHN   You are right, Conrade. I hate them all,
          but I will smile lovingly at them. Here comes
          Borachio – and he's in a hurry!
          Borachio runs into the room.

BORACHIO   Don John, I have some news. Claudio wants to
          marry Leonato's daughter!

DON JOHN   How do you know?

BORACHIO I heard your brother and Claudio talking a
        few minutes ago. Claudio wants to marry Hero,
        and Don Pedro is going to help him. It's a secret!

CONRADE Didn't they see you?

BORACHIO No. I was hiding. They didn't know that I was
        listening.

DON JOHN That brave young gentleman Claudio, and the
        beautiful Hero! How I hate them! But I can make
        trouble for them. Will you both help me?

CONRADE To the death, my lord!

DON JOHN Come, let us talk about our plans.

BORACHIO We will follow you, my lord. (*They leave.*)

'I can make trouble for them.'

ACT 2 SCENE 1

Don John tries to make trouble

*Inside Leonato's house. Leonato, Hero, Beatrice, their
servants Ursula and Margaret, and the musicians are all
getting ready for the party.*

LEONATO Now, are you all ready? Our guests will be here
in a few minutes. Ursula, Margaret – bring in the
food. Hero, my dear, you look beautiful.

BEATRICE Perhaps she'll fall in love tonight!

LEONATO What about you, Beatrice? When will you
marry?

BEATRICE Never, I hope.

HERO But why not? Don't you like men?

BEATRICE Of course I do. My father was a man, and I
liked him. My brother is a man, and I like him.

HERO (*Smiling*) Benedick is a man.

BEATRICE And I hate him! He talks too much, he laughs
too much, and…

LEONATO Here they come! Welcome, gentlemen!
*Don Pedro, Claudio, and Benedick enter,
wearing masks.*

LEONATO Musicians – start playing! Listen, everyone! I
want you all to dance and enjoy yourselves. (*The
musicians play, and some people start dancing.*)

DON PEDRO (*To Hero*) Would you like to dance with me?

HERO Perhaps. Who are you?

DON PEDRO I won't tell you my name. Come and sit down
       first! (*They go to the side of the room and talk.*)
BENEDICK (*To Beatrice*) Are you Beatrice?
BEATRICE Yes, that's right. Why, who are you?
BENEDICK I won't tell you! Someone was talking about
       you last week. He said, 'Beatrice is an angry
       old woman. Don't go near her – she's always
       arguing!' I can't remember who it was.
BEATRICE I know – it was that idiot Benedick!
BENEDICK Oh! Er – who's Benedick?
BEATRICE Don't you know him? He's the most boring
       man I've ever known. He thinks that all the
       women in Messina are in love with him. But
       everyone just laughs at him!
BENEDICK Oh. When I meet him, I'll tell him what you
       say.
       *Benedick, Beatrice, and Leonato go to the side
       of the room. Don John, Borachio, and Conrade
       enter.*
DON JOHN Borachio – is that Claudio over there, wearing
       his mask?
BORACHIO Yes, my lord. I know the way he stands.
DON JOHN Now for my plan. (*To Claudio*) You're
       Benedick, aren't you? Listen, Benedick. My
       brother, Don Pedro, is in love with Hero.
BORACHIO That's right, sir, he's going to marry her.
CLAUDIO What! Is this true? How do you know?

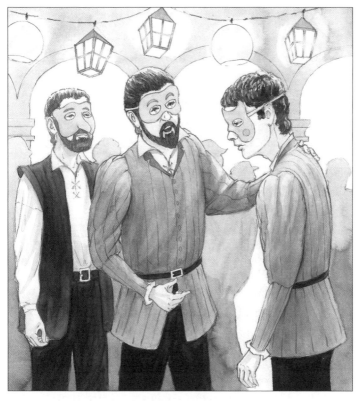

'*My brother, Don Pedro, is in love with Hero.*'

CONRADE I heard them talking a few minutes ago. Look –
        they're together now. Can't you see?

DON JOHN My brother is making a mistake, isn't he,
        Benedick? He is a prince, and he must marry a
        king's daughter. Hero is not good enough for
        him. Why don't you talk to him, Benedick? He
        will listen to you.

Don John, Borachio, and Conrade leave.
Benedick comes to talk to Claudio.

BENEDICK   Is that you, Claudio?

CLAUDIO   Yes, it's me. Let's take off our masks. (*They take them off.*) I've just heard some terrible news, Benedick. Don Pedro is going to marry Hero!

BENEDICK   What! But *you* love Hero, don't you?

CLAUDIO   I thought that Don Pedro was my friend, and wanted to help me. Oh Hero, my lost love!
Claudio leaves, and Don Pedro comes to find Benedick.

DON PEDRO   Ah, Benedick. Where's Claudio gone? Why is he in such a hurry? What's the matter?

BENEDICK   He's angry with you, Don Pedro. Why did you steal Hero from him?

DON PEDRO   But I didn't! I told Hero that Claudio loves her. She's very happy, and wants to marry him. I've talked to her father, and he agrees.

BENEDICK   I don't understand. Claudio heard that…

DON PEDRO   Here comes Claudio now, with Beatrice.
Beatrice and Claudio come over to them.

BENEDICK   Oh, no! My lord, I will do anything you ask. I will go to the end of the world, fight a hundred men, or kill a lion, but do not ask me to spend another minute with that woman! (*He leaves.*)

DON PEDRO   Claudio, I have some wonderful news.

CLAUDIO   I know. It's about Hero.

DON PEDRO   Aren't you happy? Hero wants to marry you!

CLAUDIO   Marry *me*? But – isn't she going to marry *you*?

DON PEDRO   Of course not! Here comes Leonato now.

Leonato and Hero come to talk to them.

LEONATO   Claudio, Don Pedro has spoken to me, and
I know that you love my daughter. Take her as
your wife, and be happy!

BEATRICE   Say something, Claudio!

CLAUDIO   I... I can't find the right words. (*To Hero*) Lady,
if you are mine, then I am yours.

'Lady, if you are mine, then I am yours.'

BEATRICE   (*To Hero*) Speak, cousin, or close his mouth
          with a kiss. (*Claudio and Hero kiss.*)

DON PEDRO   What about you, Beatrice? Where shall we
          find a husband for you?

BEATRICE   Don't talk to me about husbands, my lord! It's
          late. I'm going to bed. (*She leaves.*)

DON PEDRO   (*To Leonato*) I have an idea. I think that the
          best husband for Beatrice would be Benedick.

LEONATO   What! That's impossible! They argue every
          time they meet.

CLAUDIO   Benedick says that he'll never marry.

HERO   And Beatrice says that *she'll* never marry!

DON PEDRO   Listen. I have a plan. If the three of you agree
          to help me, I think that there'll soon be another
          wedding in Messina.

ACT 2 SCENE 2
Borachio has an idea

*A room in Leonato's house. Don John, Conrade, and
Borachio are talking.*

DON JOHN   What happened at the party, Conrade? Is
          Claudio angry with Don Pedro? Did they fight?

CONRADE   No, my lord. They all talked together, and
          Claudio and Hero are going to marry soon.

DON JOHN   No! We must stop them! Claudio is my

brother's friend. I don't want him to be happy. I
hate them all!

BORACHIO I have an idea, Don John. Hero has a servant
called Margaret. She is a friend of mine.

DON JOHN Go on, Borachio.

BORACHIO On the night before Hero's wedding, I'll tell
Margaret to wear Hero's clothes. I'll tell her to
go into Hero's bedroom – when Hero isn't there
– and to open the window.

CONRADE So if people see her, they'll think that she is
Hero. But why?

BORACHIO Listen. I will be in Hero's room too. When
Margaret opens the window, I'll call out loudly,
'Hero, my love, close the window and come back
to me.'

DON JOHN If Claudio sees this, he'll be very angry! He'll
never speak to Hero again.

BORACHIO My lord, you must tell Claudio and Don Pedro
to come and watch while I speak to Margaret.

CONRADE They'll think that Hero has a lover. There'll be
trouble!

DON JOHN Borachio, if this plan works, I'll pay you well –
in gold!

ACT 2 SCENE 3

A surprise for Benedick

Benedick is alone in Leonato's garden.

BENEDICK Why do people marry? Claudio is a brave
soldier, and a wonderful fighter, but now he only
talks about love. Will that ever happen to me?
No! I like women, but I'm never going to marry.
(*Don Pedro, Leonato, and Claudio enter.*) I don't
want to talk to them. If I hide behind this tree,
they won't see me. (*He hides.*)

DON PEDRO (*Quietly*) Now, you two, remember our plan.
Benedick's hiding behind the tree. Speak loudly,
and then he'll hear us.

LEONATO (*Loudly*) Don Pedro, my daughter told me a
secret this morning.

DON PEDRO What did she say, Leonato?

LEONATO That Beatrice is in love.

BENEDICK (*To himself*) What!

CLAUDIO That's right, Don Pedro. Hero told me too.
Beatrice is in love – with Benedick.

BENEDICK (*To himself*) With me? I don't believe it!

DON PEDRO But Beatrice is always laughing at Benedick.
She says that she'll never fall in love with any man!

LEONATO She loves him, but she doesn't want to tell him.

CLAUDIO Leonato is right, Don Pedro. Once she wrote a
love letter to Benedick, but she didn't send it.

DON PEDRO   So Beatrice loves Benedick. What a surprise!
      But if she doesn't tell him, he will never know.
CLAUDIO   And if she tells him, he'll laugh at her. What
      can she do? She's very unhappy.
LEONATO   She's a beautiful girl.
CLAUDIO   And she's kind.
DON PEDRO   And she's clever.
CLAUDIO   So why does she love Benedick? (*They laugh.*)
BENEDICK   (*To himself*) What! Why are they laughing?

'*So Beatrice loves Benedick.*'

Leonato, Claudio, and Don Pedro leave.
Benedick comes out from behind the tree.

BENEDICK I can't believe it! Beatrice loves me! That's what Leonato said – it must be true! They all think that she is beautiful, and clever. Perhaps they are right… but why does she always laugh at me?

BEATRICE (*Entering*) Dinner is ready. Are you coming in?

BENEDICK Ah, Beatrice! I've heard a little secret.

BEATRICE What are you talking about? Oh, it doesn't matter. I'm hungry, so I'm going inside. If you want dinner, come in now. (*She leaves.*)

BENEDICK Oh, Beatrice! She loves me – that's why she came here to find me. The others were right. She is beautiful, and kind, too. Oh, how I love her! Beatrice – wait for me! I'll come with you!

ACT 3 SCENE 1

A surprise for Beatrice

Hero, Margaret, and Ursula are in Leonato's garden.

HERO Margaret, go and find Beatrice. Tell her to come out into the garden.

MARGARET What shall I say to her?

HERO Tell her that Ursula and I are talking about her.

URSULA That's right, tell her that she must come and listen secretly. (*Margaret leaves.*)

HERO Now, remember the plan, Ursula. We must talk about Benedick, and how much he loves Beatrice.

URSULA Sh! Here she comes now. (*Beatrice enters.*)

BEATRICE (*To herself*) Margaret says that Hero and
Ursula are talking about me. How strange! I'll
hide behind this tree and listen. (*She hides.*)

HERO (*To Ursula*) Remember, Ursula – speak loudly!

URSULA (*Loudly*) So Benedick's in love, is he?

HERO That's right. His friends told me. He's in love
with Beatrice.

BEATRICE (*To herself*) What! Benedick – in love with me?

URSULA Shall we tell Beatrice?

HERO No, Ursula, we mustn't tell her. If she hears that
Benedick loves her, she'll only laugh at him.

BEATRICE (*To herself*) What! No, I won't!

'*What! Benedick – in love with me?*'

URSULA Poor Benedick! He's in love, but he can't say
        anything to Beatrice.

HERO   No. He's very unhappy.

URSULA If he's lucky, perhaps he will meet someone
        kinder than Beatrice.

HERO   I hope so. He's a good man. He's very brave.

URSULA And he's very good-looking. I think he's the best
        man in Italy.

HERO   No, Ursula, Claudio is the best man in Italy.
        That's why I'm going to marry him!

URSULA They are both fine men. Come, my lady, let's go
        inside.

        Hero and Ursula leave. Beatrice comes out.

BEATRICE Can this really be true? Does Benedick love
        me? Everyone thinks that I hate him, but it's not
        true. Hero and Ursula are right – he is brave, and
        good-looking. Oh, Benedick! I love you!

ACT 3 SCENE 2

Claudio hears a terrible secret

*A room in Leonato's house. Leonato, Don Pedro,
Claudio, and Benedick are talking.*

DON PEDRO Leonato, I have enjoyed staying with you. But
        tomorrow, after Claudio's wedding, I must go
        home.

LEONATO Stay as long as you want, Don Pedro. You must

stay too, Benedick.

BENEDICK Sorry? I wasn't listening, my lord.

DON PEDRO What's the matter, Benedick? What are you
        thinking about?

BENEDICK Nothing, my lord.

CLAUDIO Perhaps he's in love.

BENEDICK Of course not! I – er – I've got toothache.

DON PEDRO Toothache! I don't believe you, Benedick. I
        agree with Claudio. I think you're in love.

CLAUDIO I think I know someone who is dying of love for
        Benedick. (*Claudio and Don Pedro laugh.*)

BENEDICK I'm not listening, Claudio! My lord Leonato,
        can I talk to you? (*Benedick and Leonato leave.*)

DON PEDRO They're going to talk about Beatrice!

CLAUDIO Your plan has gone well, Don Pedro. (*Don John
        enters.*) Look – here's your brother.

DON PEDRO It's good to see you, brother John. How are
        you?

DON JOHN I have some bad news, my friends. Claudio,
        are you planning to marry tomorrow?

CLAUDIO Yes, I am. Everyone knows that I am going to
        marry Leonato's daughter, Hero.

DON JOHN I'm sorry, but I must tell you something that
        will hurt you – the truth about Hero.

DON PEDRO What are you talking about?

DON JOHN She has a secret life. She doesn't love you.

CLAUDIO That's a terrible thing to say!

DON JOHN Perhaps she says that she loves you. But she
          has many, many lovers. You are not the only one.
DON PEDRO My brother, how can you say that? Hero is a
          sweet young girl. She wants to marry Claudio.
          She doesn't love any other man.
DON JOHN I know that this is bad news for you. But if
          you come with me tonight, you'll understand.
CLAUDIO What do you mean? What will we see?
DON JOHN One of Hero's lovers is going to visit her at
          midnight tonight.
DON PEDRO What? The night before her wedding?
DON JOHN Come with me to Hero's window tonight, and
          you will see that I am right.

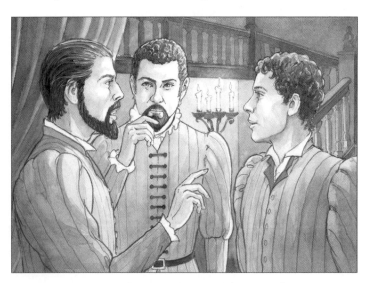

'Come with me to Hero's window tonight.'

CLAUDIO This is terrible. If this is true, I will never marry
       Hero. (*Claudio and Don Pedro leave.*)

DON JOHN Borachio! (*Borachio enters.*) You remember the
       plan, don't you?

BORACHIO Yes, my lord. I'll be in Hero's bedroom at
       midnight tonight.

DON JOHN And will Margaret be there?

BORACHIO Yes, my lord. She'll wear Hero's clothes, and
       she'll open the window.

DON JOHN Good. Remember that Claudio and Don Pedro
       will be in the garden, watching.

BORACHIO When Margaret goes to the window, I'll call
       out to her and tell her that I love her.

DON JOHN Good. There will be trouble, Borachio!
       Claudio is going to be very unhappy – and so is
       Hero!

ACT 3 SCENE 3

The police find two criminals

*A street, late at night. Dogberry is talking to Verges and
three other policemen.*

DOGBERRY Now, you know what your job is, don't you?

1ST POLICEMAN Yes, sir, we're policemen.

DOGBERRY I know that you're policemen! I mean, do you
       know what you must do?

2ND POLICEMAN Yes, sir. We must walk around Messina. If

we see any trouble, we must stop it.

VERGES That's right. If you meet any thieves, tell them to stop stealing at once.

3RD POLICEMAN What if they don't stop, sir?

DOGBERRY Well, tell them to leave Messina and steal from another town.

2ND POLICEMAN And if we find anyone shouting or making too much noise, we'll tell them to be quiet.

VERGES That's right. We don't want any trouble.

1ST POLICEMAN And we'll go to all the public houses.

VERGES That's a good idea. Walking around Messina all night is very boring. It's cold, too.

DOGBERRY No, Verges, he means that they'll go to the public houses to see if there's any trouble.

3RD POLICEMAN That's right, sir. If we find any people who have drunk too much, we'll tell them to go home.

DOGBERRY That's right, men. Now, Verges, come with me. (*Dogberry and Verges leave.*)

1ST POLICEMAN Let's see if we can find any criminals.

2ND POLICEMAN Wait a minute! I can hear voices.

3RD POLICEMAN Let's hide behind this wall.

They hide. Borachio and Conrade enter.

CONRADE A hundred pounds? In gold?

BORACHIO That's right, Don John's given me a hundred pounds. I've just been to Hero's room.

CONRADE Was Margaret there?

BORACHIO Yes, and she was wearing Hero's clothes. I
shouted, 'Hero, my love, give me a kiss!'
(*He laughs.*)

CONRADE Were Claudio and Don Pedro watching?

BORACHIO Yes, they were in the garden with Don John.

CONRADE Claudio won't marry Hero now, will he?

BORACHIO Never! That's why Don John has given me a
hundred pounds. He's very happy – and so am I!
Here – let's have a drink!
*He takes a bottle from his pocket. The policemen
jump out and take hold of the two men.*

'Were Claudio and Don Pedro watching?'

1ST POLICEMAN Stop, both of you! Stay where you are, in the Prince's name!

CONRADE Take your hands off us! We haven't done anything wrong.

2ND POLICEMAN Oh yes, you have! We heard everything. You have said terrible things about Lady Hero.

3RD POLICEMAN And they're thieves. This man has stolen a hundred pounds.

BORACHIO No, I haven't! It's my money!

2ND POLICEMAN Let's take them to the prison. Dogberry will want to ask them some questions.

3RD POLICEMAN Come on, you two! Come with us!

ACT 4 SCENE 1
Hero's wedding day

Outside the church. Father Francis, Leonato, Hero, Beatrice, and Benedick are ready for the wedding.

LEONATO Hero, my dear, this is a very happy day for me.

HERO And for me too, father.

Don Pedro, Claudio, and Don John enter.

LEONATO Here comes Claudio! Father Francis, the wedding can begin now.

FATHER FRANCIS Claudio and Hero, you have come here today to marry. Hero, do you agree to be Claudio's wife?

HERO I do.

FATHER FRANCIS And Claudio, do you agree to be Hero's
   husband?

CLAUDIO No! (*Everyone shouts in surprise.*)

LEONATO What? Claudio, you mustn't joke like this.

HERO My love, what's the matter?

CLAUDIO You heard what I said. Leonato, I will not
   marry your daughter.

LEONATO This is terrible! What's happened, Claudio?

CLAUDIO Everyone thinks that Hero is a good, sweet
   young girl. It's not true. She has many lovers.

BEATRICE How can you say that about my cousin?

LEONATO I don't believe you, Claudio! Don Pedro, why is
   he saying these things?

'*I will not marry your daughter.*'

DON PEDRO I'm sorry, Leonato, but Claudio is right.

HERO No! Listen to me, all of you! Claudio is the only man that I love!

DON PEDRO A man was in Hero's room last night. We heard them laughing, and we saw them kissing at the window.

DON JOHN It's true, Leonato. One of Hero's lovers visited her last night. It has happened many times.

HERO I talked with no man last night, my lord.
Claudio, Don Pedro, and Don John leave. Hero faints.

BEATRICE (*Holding Hero*) Hero! My dear cousin!

BENEDICK How is she? She's not dead, is she?

FATHER FRANCIS No, she's alive. She's opening her eyes.

LEONATO This is the worst day of my life. What are we going to do?

BENEDICK Sir, I just do not know what to say.

BEATRICE I'm sure that Hero hasn't done anything wrong.

FATHER FRANCIS I agree with you. Hero, did anyone visit you last night?

HERO No, of course not. Kill me if you like, but please don't believe Claudio and Don Pedro!

FATHER FRANCIS Listen. I have a plan. We'll tell Don Pedro, Claudio, and all the others that Hero is dead.

LEONATO Dead? Why, Father?

FATHER FRANCIS If they think that Hero is dead, they will
          not be angry with her any more. Then, perhaps,
          they will be able to find out the truth.

LEONATO Very well, Father, I agree. We will tell everyone
          that Hero is dead.

          Everyone except Benedick and Beatrice leaves.

BENEDICK Don't cry, Beatrice.

BEATRICE This is a terrible day for my cousin Hero.

BENEDICK Beatrice, there's something that I must tell you.
          I love you more than anything in the world. And
          I know that you love me.

BEATRICE What! How do you know? Who told you?

BENEDICK That doesn't matter. You love me, don't you?

BEATRICE I don't know what to say. (*They kiss.*) Yes, I
          love you with all my heart.

BENEDICK Beatrice, I will do anything for you.

BEATRICE Kill Claudio.

BENEDICK What? No, not for the world! Claudio is my
          friend.

BEATRICE Then you do not really love me! My cousin's
          heart is broken, and it's all because of your
          friends, the brave Claudio and the good Don
          Pedro!

BENEDICK Beatrice, I'm sorry about Hero. But I love *you*,
          and that's the most important thing.

BEATRICE You love your friends more than me. Go,
          Benedick, and leave me alone.

'Beatrice, I will do anything for you.'

BENEDICK But aren't Don Pedro and Claudio telling
     the truth? They said that there was someone in
     Hero's room last night.

BEATRICE If they believe that, they are stupid.

BENEDICK I'm sorry, Beatrice. You are right. Claudio has
     hurt your cousin badly. I will fight him, and one
     of us will die. (*He kisses her hand and leaves.*)

Dogberry talks to the prisoners

Borachio and Conrade are in prison. Dogberry and Verges have come to ask them some questions. The policemen are watching.

DOGBERRY Where are the criminals?

VERGES They are here, sir, in front of you.

DOGBERRY What are your names?

BORACHIO My name is Borachio, and this is my friend Conrade.

DOGBERRY Well, Borachio and Conrade, I have heard that you have said bad things about a lady. Also, you are thieves and you drink too much. Is this true?

BORACHIO No, sir. We haven't done anything wrong.

CONRADE That's right, sir. We were walking along the street last night when the police suddenly stopped us. I don't know why they stopped us, sir.

BORACHIO We'd like to go home, please, sir. We don't like being in prison.

DOGBERRY Oh. Verges, there has been a mistake. These men say that they aren't criminals.

VERGES Why don't we ask the policemen what they think, sir?

DOGBERRY That's a good idea, Verges. Well, men, what happened last night?

1ST POLICEMAN While these two men were talking, sir, we were hiding behind a wall.

2ND POLICEMAN   We heard everything that they said, sir.

3RD POLICEMAN   One of them said that he was in Lady
    Hero's bedroom with Margaret, her servant.

VERGES   In Hero's bedroom? Perhaps they are thieves?

3RD POLICEMAN   One of them had a hundred pounds.

DOGBERRY   Ah! So they *are* thieves!

BORACHIO   That's not true, sir! (*To Conrade*) This man is
    an idiot, Conrade. What can we do?

DOGBERRY   What! I heard you! Verges, that man called me
    an idiot. Write it down!

VERGES   Yes, sir. (*He writes.*) You are an idiot, sir.

DOGBERRY   That's right. I am an idiot, Verges, remember
    that. These two men are criminals, I think.

'*We heard everything that they said, sir.*'

VERGES What shall we do with them, sir? Shall we leave
          them in prison, or shall we tell them to go home?
DOGBERRY We must ask Lord Leonato – he will decide.
          Let's take them to see him now!

Borachio tells the truth

Don Pedro and Claudio are walking along the street.

DON PEDRO Claudio, have you heard that Hero is dead?
CLAUDIO Yes, I have. But perhaps it's better for her to be
          dead than alive.
          Leonato enters.
DON PEDRO Good morning, my lord.
LEONATO Good? Nothing is good any more. My
          daughter, my only child, is dead.
CLAUDIO Sir, we are sorry about Hero's death.
LEONATO How can you say that? You killed her!
CLAUDIO That's not true! I didn't want her to die!
DON PEDRO Leonato, you must remember that we saw
          Hero with another man the night before the
          wedding.
LEONATO Ha! I don't believe you. And I'll find out the
          truth!
          He leaves, and Benedick enters.
CLAUDIO It's good to see you, Benedick.

BENEDICK (*Angrily*) Claudio, you and I are friends no
more.

DON PEDRO What do you mean? Are you joking?

BENEDICK No, I'm not joking. Claudio, you have killed a
sweet lady. And I am going to kill you.

CLAUDIO If you want to fight, I'm not afraid.

BENEDICK When you decide on the time and the place,
send a messenger to tell me. We will meet, and
we will fight. And one of us will die.

DON PEDRO Benedick, what are you saying? Claudio didn't
kill Hero.

BENEDICK My lord, do you know that your brother Don
John has left Messina? I must go now, too.
(*He leaves.*)

CLAUDIO If he wants to fight, I'm ready!

DON PEDRO No, you mustn't fight. I'll talk to Benedick.
So my brother has left Messina. How strange!
*Dogberry, Verges, the policemen, and the
prisoners enter.*

CLAUDIO Look! There are your brother's servants.

DON PEDRO What's the matter, Dogberry? What have
these men done?

DOGBERRY They have done many things, sir. First, they
are criminals. Third, they are thieves.

VERGES And sixth, they drink too much. Second, and
last, they have said bad things about a lady, Lord
Leonato's daughter.

'Claudio, you and I are friends no more.'

DOGBERRY And fourth, this man said that I was an idiot.
Verges, go and find Lord Leonato and bring him
here. (*Verges leaves.*)

CLAUDIO (*Laughing*) These men are too clever for me,
Don Pedro. I don't understand them.

DON PEDRO Neither do I. What's happened, Borachio?

BORACHIO My lords, do you remember seeing Hero and
her lover the night before the wedding?

CLAUDIO Of course we do!

BORACHIO The woman wasn't Hero, sir. It was her
servant Margaret. And the man wasn't her lover.
It was me.

CLAUDIO What! I don't believe it!

CONRADE It's true, sir. Don John wanted to hurt you and
Hero. He paid Borachio a lot of money to do it.

DON PEDRO So Hero didn't do anything wrong.

CLAUDIO Oh, sweet Hero! What have I done? I'm sorry!

DON PEDRO She's dead, Claudio. She'll never come back.

Leonato and Verges enter.

BORACHIO My lord, I'm sorry. I killed your daughter.

LEONATO Not you alone, Borachio. Four men killed my daughter. You are one of them. Don John is another. The other two are here now: the brave Claudio and the good Don Pedro.

CLAUDIO My lord, we are both very sorry. But we believed Don John when he told us about Hero.

DON PEDRO We made a terrible mistake, Leonato.

'Oh, sweet Hero! What have I done?'

LEONATO Claudio, you killed my daughter, but I am not
         going to kill you. My brother has a daughter. She
         is just like Hero. Will you marry her?

CLAUDIO Of course, my lord! I will do anything you ask.

LEONATO Claudio, Don Pedro, come to my house
         tomorrow morning. Until then, goodbye.

ACT 5 SCENE 2
Beatrice and Benedick hear the news

Beatrice and Benedick are in Leonato's garden.

BENEDICK Beatrice, I love you. I think that I have always
          loved you.

BEATRICE I love you too, Benedick. But do you remember
          what I asked you to do?

BENEDICK Yes, my love. I have talked to Claudio. I will
          fight him, and kill him if I can.

BEATRICE Good. My cousin Hero is still very ill.

BENEDICK Beatrice, my love, when did you first fall in love
          with me? And why?

BEATRICE I didn't want to fall in love with you, or
          anyone. But when I knew that…
          Ursula enters, running.

URSULA My lord! My lady! There's some exciting news
        about Hero! And Don John's servants are in
        trouble! Come inside and hear about it!

ACT 5 SCENE 3
Two weddings

Leonato, Father Francis, Beatrice, Hero, Benedick,
Margaret, the servants, and musicians are all at
Leonato's house.

LEONATO You were right, Father Francis. My daughter
didn't do anything wrong.

FATHER FRANCIS Of course she didn't.

LEONATO It was Don John who planned all this. But he
has escaped, and nobody knows where he is.

BENEDICK I told Claudio to be ready to fight me, but now
I hope that we will be friends.

LEONATO I hope so, too. Claudio will be here soon.
Beatrice, Hero, Margaret – put on your masks.
Don Pedro and Claudio enter.

LEONATO Welcome, gentlemen. Claudio, here is the new
wife that I have found for you.

CLAUDIO Can I see her, my lord?

LEONATO First you must agree to marry her.
Hero comes up to Claudio.

FATHER FRANCIS This is the lady. Will you marry her?

CLAUDIO Yes, I will. (*Hero takes off her mask.*) Hero!

DON PEDRO But Hero is dead!

CLAUDIO Hero, my love!

HERO Claudio, when you said those terrible things to
me on our wedding day, I nearly died. But I am
alive, and I still love you.

FATHER FRANCIS　This is a happy day! Come with me to the
church, everyone. It's time for the wedding!

BENEDICK　Wait. There will be two weddings today, Father
Francis, not just one. Where is Beatrice?

BEATRICE　(*Taking off her mask*) I'm here, Benedick.

BENEDICK　Beatrice, will you marry me?

'There will be two weddings today.'

LEONATO This is wonderful!

DON PEDRO They're in love! What did I tell you, Claudio? Our friend Benedick, the married man!

HERO Well, Beatrice, are you going to answer him?

BEATRICE Benedick, I'll marry you if it makes you happy.

BENEDICK No, no, Beatrice, if you marry me, it will make *you* happy.

CLAUDIO Don't start arguing, my friends!

BENEDICK Claudio is right. Let's not argue – let's kiss.

They kiss, as a messenger enters.

MESSENGER My lords, the police have found Don John. They are bringing him back to Messina.

DON PEDRO We'll think about that tomorrow. Today, we must think about these weddings.

BENEDICK Let's have a party first! Musicians – start playing! Dance, everybody! Enjoy yourselves!

The musicians play, and everyone dances.

GLOSSARY

argue *(v)* to talk or shout angrily when you don't agree with
   someone
believe *(v)* to feel sure that something is true or right
brave *(adj)* not afraid of anything
cousin *(n)* your uncle's or aunt's child
enter *(v)* to come in
faint *(v)* to fall down suddenly because you are ill or get bad
   news
fall in love *(v)* to find out, suddenly, that you love someone
gentleman *(n)* a man of good family
good-looking *(adj)* beautiful, handsome
hate *(v)* opposite of 'to love'
heart *(n)* (in this play) a person's feelings and hopes
idea *(n)* a plan that comes into your head suddenly
idiot *(n)* a stupid person
joke *(n)* to say (or to do) something funny
kiss *(v & n)* to touch someone with the lips in a loving way
lady *(n)* a title for a woman of good family
lion *(n)* a large and dangerous wild animal found in Africa (we
   say 'as brave as a lion')
lord *(n)* a title for a man of good family
mask *(n)* a cover that you put over your face to hide it
messenger *(n)* someone who brings news or information
musician *(n)* someone who plays a musical instrument
priest *(n)* a person who works for the church, a church leader
prince *(n)* the son of a king or queen
public house *(n)* a place where people meet, often in the
   evenings, to drink and eat

servant *(n)*   someone who works (for example, cooking or cleaning) in another person's house

sir *(n)*   a polite way to speak to a man who is more important than you

toothache *(n)*   when one of your teeth hurts

truth *(n)*   something that is true

war *(n)*   fighting between countries or large groups of people

wedding *(n)*   when a man and a woman marry (often in a church)

Much Ado About Nothing

ACTIVITIES

ACTIVITIES

Before Reading

1 The title of the play is *Much Ado About Nothing*. What kind of story do you think it is? Tick one box for each sentence.

	YES	NO	PERHAPS
1 A story with a sad ending.	☐	☐	☐
2 A story about love.	☐	☐	☐
3 A murder story.	☐	☐	☐
4 A funny story.	☐	☐	☐

2 Read the back cover. How much do you know now about the story? Fill in the gaps with these names.

Don John / Leonato / Benedick / Claudio

1 _____ is in love with Hero.

2 _____ doesn't want Claudio and Hero to be happy.

3 _____ often argues with Beatrice.

4 _____ is Hero's father.

3 Which words do you think you will find in this story? Why won't you find all of them?

brave, dance, daughter, ghost, good-looking, hate, hide, kiss, lady, love, mask, photograph, potato, taxi, tree, wedding

ACTIVITIES

While Reading

Read Act 1. Are these sentences true or false? Rewrite the false sentences with the correct information.

1 A lot of soldiers were hurt in the war.
2 Hero and Beatrice are sisters.
3 Beatrice often laughs at Benedick.
4 Don John and Don Pedro are brothers.
5 Claudio falls in love with Beatrice.
6 Don John loves his brother.
7 Don John wants to make trouble for Claudio and Hero.
8 Borachio and Conrade are Don Pedro's servants.

Read Act 2. Who said these words, and to whom?

1 'Perhaps she'll fall in love tonight!'
2 'Would you like to dance with me?'
3 'Why did you steal Hero from him?'
4 'Take her as your wife, and be happy!'
5 'Lady, if you are mine, then I am yours.'
6 'Speak, cousin, or close his mouth with a kiss.'
7 'If this plan works, I'll pay you well – in gold!'
8 'Wait for me! I'll come with you!'

Read Act 3. Choose the best question-word for these questions, and then answer them.

how much / what / where / who / why

The night before Hero's wedding,

1 … did Borachio go?

2 … did Margaret wear?

3 … was watching from the garden?

4 … money did Don John give Borachio?

5 … was Don John happy?

Read Act 4. What happened on Hero's wedding day? Complete this summary with these words from the play.

alive, believe, cousin, dead, fainted, happily, kill, marry, plan, terrible, truth

Hero and her father were waiting _____ at the church. But when Claudio arrived, he said that he didn't want to _____ Hero. Claudio said some _____ things about Hero. Beatrice and Leonato didn't _____ him, but Don Pedro said that Claudio was telling the _____. When Claudio left, Hero _____, but she was still _____. Father Francis had a _____. He decided to tell Claudio and the others that Hero was _____. Later, when Beatrice was alone with Benedick, she told him to _____ Claudio. She was angry because her _____ was very unhappy.

Before you read Act 5, what do you think happens to these people? Choose one answer for each sentence.

1 Borachio and Conrade *tell the truth about Don John's plan / escape from Messina / go to prison.*
2 Hero *says she will never marry / dies of a broken heart / marries Claudio.*
3 Claudio *marries Hero / marries another woman / fights Benedick and dies.*
4 Beatrice *kills Claudio / marries Benedick / marries another man.*

Read Act 5, then match these parts of sentences.

1 Benedick wanted to kill Claudio, but…
2 Borachio told Claudio the truth about…
3 Leonato said that he had…
4 Leonato said that his brother's daughter…
5 Claudio agreed to marry his new wife, but…
6 Claudio was surprised and happy when…

7 the night before Hero's wedding.
8 he couldn't see her face at first.
9 a new wife for Claudio.
10 Hero took off her mask.
11 Claudio wasn't afraid.
12 was just like Hero.

ACTIVITIES

_____

After Reading

1 Perhaps this is what five people in the play are thinking. Who
   are they, and what is happening in the play at the moment?

   1 'What a sweet, beautiful girl! I want her to be my wife!
     But her father is an important man. Perhaps he won't
     agree?'

   2 'Hero's saying that Benedick loves me! That's wonderful!
     But why hasn't he told me? I must see him at once!'

   3 'That's Hero! She's talking to a man, in her room!
     They're laughing and kissing! This is terrible. My
     brother was right.'

   4 'I can't believe it! What does he mean? Why is he saying
     all these terrible things about my little girl? And look at
     her now – she's fainting!'

   5 'When I take my mask off, he'll be surprised – he thinks
     I've died! I hope he'll be happy too. He said some
     terrible things about me, but I still love him and want to
     marry him!'

2 Here are some other titles for the play. Which are good and
   which are not good? Can you explain why?

   A Death and Two Weddings   *The Lion of Messina*
   The Married Man   *Love Wins in the End*
   Don John's Plan   *Behind the Mask*

3 **After her wedding, perhaps Beatrice wrote this letter to a close friend. Complete her letter with these names.**

Borachio / Hero / Benedick / Don John / Margaret / Don Pedro / Claudio

Dear Sarah,

What a week! When the war finished, Don Pedro and his friends came back to Messina. A young soldier called _____ fell in love with my cousin _____, and they decided to marry! But _____ didn't want them to be happy. He told Claudio and _____ that Hero had many lovers. They believed him, but of course I didn't! Later, Don John's servant _____ told the truth – the people in Hero's room were Borachio and Hero's servant _____. In the end, Claudio married Hero – and I married _____! Can you believe it?

Your loving friend, Beatrice

4 **Dogberry wrote this report, but it's full of mistakes. Rewrite it with the correct information.**

Yesterday afternoon, some of my policemen were walking around Messina. They heard three men talking; their names were Borachio and Leonato. One said, 'I've just been to Lady Beatrice's room!' He was in her room because his master, Don Pedro, wanted to stop the wedding between Beatrice and Benedick. Later, I met the criminals and answered some of their questions. They called Verges an idiot!

5 There are eleven words from the play hidden in this word search. The words go from left to right, and from top to bottom. Can you find them all?

W	I	V	O	B	U	T	F	A	P
E	M	U	S	I	C	I	A	N	R
D	O	N	I	D	E	B	I	L	I
D	N	E	B	I	C	R	N	E	N
I	C	C	K	O	A	H	T	P	C
N	T	O	O	T	H	A	C	H	E
G	L	U	N	V	L	R	W	A	R
M	A	S	K	R	O	G	S	T	E
U	G	I	A	C	R	U	C	E	N
R	D	N	E	K	V	E	Y	P	S

Match the hidden words with these meanings:

1 _____ to talk or shout angrily
2 _____ your uncle's or aunt's child
3 _____ when one of your teeth hurts
4 _____ when a man and woman marry
5 _____ someone who plays a musical instrument
6 _____ fighting between countries
7 _____ to fall down suddenly because you are ill
8 _____ the son of a king or queen
9 _____ a cover that you put over your face
10 _____ a stupid person
11 _____ opposite of 'to love'

6 **When Don John comes back to Messina, Don Pedro talks to him (see page 38). Put their conversation in the correct order and write in their names. Don Pedro speaks first (number 6).**

1 _____ 'But it was my servant's idea to go to Hero's room with Margaret. I didn't want him to do it!'

2 _____ 'That's not true! You left Messina because you didn't want the police to find you!'

3 _____ 'No! Please! I don't want to go to prison! I'll never hurt your friends again. Remember, we are brothers – your friends are my friends!'

4 _____ 'I didn't run away. I wanted to visit a friend in Rome—'

5 _____ 'Did I give him some gold? I can't remember.'

6 _____ 'Why did you try to run away from Messina?'

7 _____ 'You have! You tried to hurt my friends. You wanted to stop the wedding. Hero nearly died!'

8 _____ 'Listen. If you do anything bad again, you will go to prison for a very long time.'

9 _____ 'Borachio has told us everything. You gave him money to do it, didn't you?'

10 _____ 'But I haven't done anything wrong!'

7 **Choose some people from the play, and write a sentence about each person. Did you feel sorry for anyone? Did you feel angry with anyone? Who was your favourite person in the play? Why?**

ABOUT THE AUTHOR

William Shakespeare (1564–1616) was born in Stratford-upon-Avon, a small town in central England. He went to school in Stratford, and he married when he was only eighteen years old. A few years later, he moved to London, while his wife and children stayed in Stratford. He worked as an actor, and soon started writing plays and poetry. At that time, theatres were new and exciting places. There were only a few theatres in England, and they were all in London.

Shakespeare wrote more than thirty plays, and Queen Elizabeth I often saw his plays.

When he was in his late forties, Shakespeare returned to Stratford for a quiet life with his family away from the theatre. He died in 1616, when he was only fifty-two years old.

Much Ado About Nothing was first published in 1600, and is one of Shakespeare's most popular comedies to this day.

OXFORD BOOKWORMS LIBRARY

Classics • Crime & Mystery • Factfiles • Fantasy & Horror
Human Interest • Playscripts • Thriller & Adventure
True Stories • World Stories

The OXFORD BOOKWORMS LIBRARY provides enjoyable reading in English, with a wide range of classic and modern fiction, non-fiction, and plays. It includes original and adapted texts in seven carefully graded language stages, which take learners from beginner to advanced level. An overview is given on the next pages.

All Stage 1 titles are available as audio recordings, as well as over eighty other titles from Starter to Stage 6. All Starters and many titles at Stages 1 to 4 are specially recommended for younger learners. Every Bookworm is illustrated, and Starters and Factfiles have full-colour illustrations.

The OXFORD BOOKWORMS LIBRARY also offers extensive support. Each book contains an introduction to the story, notes about the author, a glossary, and activities. Additional resources include tests and worksheets, and answers for these and for the activities in the books. There is advice on running a class library, using audio recordings, and the many ways of using Oxford Bookworms in reading programmes. Resource materials are available on the website <www.oup.com/elt/gradedreaders>.

The *Oxford Bookworms Collection* is a series for advanced learners. It consists of volumes of short stories by well-known authors, both classic and modern. Texts are not abridged or adapted in any way, but carefully selected to be accessible to the advanced student.

You can find details and a full list of titles in the *Oxford Bookworms Library Catalogue* and *Oxford English Language Teaching Catalogues*, and on the website <www.oup.com/elt/gradedreaders>.

THE OXFORD BOOKWORMS LIBRARY
GRADING AND SAMPLE EXTRACTS

STARTER • 250 HEADWORDS

present simple – present continuous – imperative –
can/cannot, *must* – *going to* (future) – simple gerunds …

Her phone is ringing – but where is it?

Sally gets out of bed and looks in her bag. No phone.
She looks under the bed. No phone. Then she looks behind
the door. There is her phone. Sally picks up her phone and
answers it. *Sally's Phone*

STAGE 1 • 400 HEADWORDS

… past simple – coordination with *and*, *but*, *or* –
subordination with *before*, *after*, *when*, *because*, *so* …

I knew him in Persia. He was a famous builder and I
worked with him there. For a time I was his friend, but
not for long. When he came to Paris, I came after him –
I wanted to watch him. He was a very clever, very
dangerous man. *The Phantom of the Opera*

STAGE 2 • 700 HEADWORDS

… present perfect – *will* (future) – *(don't) have to, must not, could* –
comparison of adjectives – simple *if* clauses – past continuous –
tag questions – *ask/tell* + infinitive …

While I was writing these words in my diary, I decided
what to do. I must try to escape. I shall try to get down the
wall outside. The window is high above the ground, but
I have to try. I shall take some of the gold with me – if I
escape, perhaps it will be helpful later. *Dracula*

STAGE 3 • 1000 HEADWORDS

... should, may – present perfect continuous – *used to* – past perfect –
causative – relative clauses – indirect statements ...

Of course, it was most important that no one should see
Colin, Mary, or Dickon entering the secret garden. So Colin
gave orders to the gardeners that they must all keep away
from that part of the garden in future. *The Secret Garden*

STAGE 4 • 1400 HEADWORDS

... past perfect continuous – passive (simple forms) –
would conditional clauses – indirect questions –
relatives with *where/when* – gerunds after prepositions/phrases ...

I was glad. Now Hyde could not show his face to the world
again. If he did, every honest man in London would be proud
to report him to the police. *Dr Jekyll and Mr Hyde*

STAGE 5 • 1800 HEADWORDS

... future continuous – future perfect –
passive (modals, continuous forms) –
would have conditional clauses – modals + perfect infinitive ...

If he had spoken Estella's name, I would have hit him. I was so
angry with him, and so depressed about my future, that I could
not eat the breakfast. Instead I went straight to the old house.
Great Expectations

STAGE 6 • 2500 HEADWORDS

... passive (infinitives, gerunds) – advanced modal meanings –
clauses of concession, condition

When I stepped up to the piano, I was confident. It was as if I
knew that the prodigy side of me really did exist. And when I
started to play, I was so caught up in how lovely I looked that I
didn't worry how I would sound. *The Joy Luck Club*

BOOKWORMS · PLAYSCRIPTS · STAGE 2

The Importance of Being Earnest

OSCAR WILDE

Retold by Susan Kingsley

Algernon knows that his friend Jack does not always tell the truth. For example, in town his name is Ernest, while in the country he calls himself Jack. And who is the girl who gives him presents 'from little Cecily, with all her love'?

But when the beautiful Gwendolen Fairfax says that she can only love a man whose name is Ernest, Jack decides to change his name, and become Ernest forever. Then Cecily agrees to marry Algernon, but only if his name is Ernest, too, and things become a little difficult for the two young men.

This famous play by Oscar Wilde is one of the finest comedies in the English language.

BOOKWORMS · PLAYSCRIPTS · STAGE 2

Hamlet

WILLIAM SHAKESPEARE

Retold by Alistair McCallum

Why does Hamlet, the young Prince of Denmark, look so sad? Why does he often say strange things? His family and friends are worried about him. Perhaps he is mad!

But Hamlet thinks that he has discovered a terrible secret about a recent crime in his family. Now he has no time for Ophelia, the sweet girl who loves him, or his friends, who were at school with him. He sits alone, and thinks, and plans. What will he decide to do? Will he ever be happy again?

This famous play by William Shakespeare, written in about 1600, is one of the finest in the English language.